F
Haa

WASHINGTON-CENTRAL SCHOOL

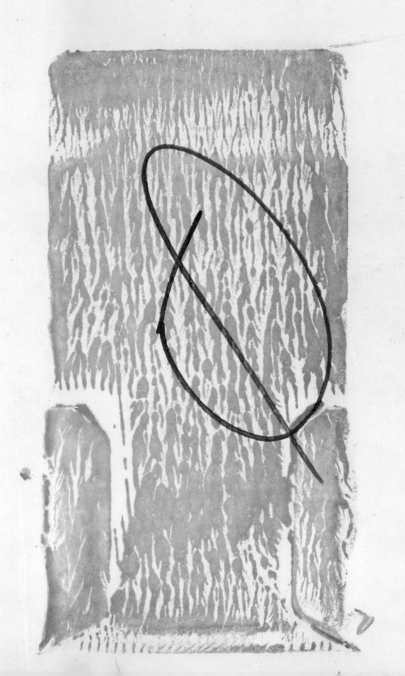

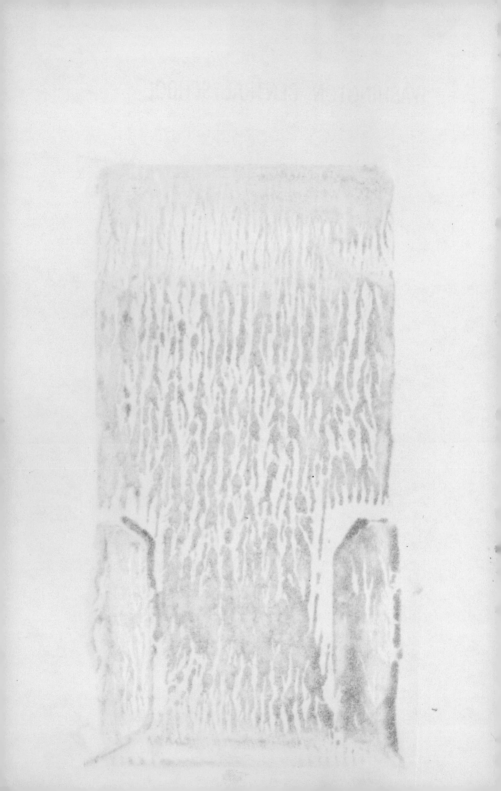

IOWA HANNAH

IOWA HANNAH

By May A. Heath

Illustrated by Charles Walker

HASTINGS HOUSE
Publishers

NEW YORK 22

To My Grandmother

Acknowledgment

I wish to acknowledge my indebtedness for information and ideas to my mother, Mrs. George A. Van Duyn, to the Reverend J. T. Wade, Miss Jean McKellar, Mrs. Edward Roebuck, Mrs. Irene Smith, and Mr. Horace Sherman.

In the main the material of this book relates true experiences of my mother's family. There are incidental variations as to names, dates, and places for the purpose of maintaining continuity.

7

Contents

Preface

Grandma and Grandpa Van Duyn lived in the same house we children did but in a separate part—a comfortable living room and bedroom that my father had added to our home. Grandma's living room, so different from Mother's, drew me as if by magic. Grandma herself was different, too. She was *always there*, and she always had plenty of time to talk.

Munching cookies or apples, I would look in the living-room door to her low rocking chair by the bay window. If she was still napping in her bedroom, I tiptoed in and wandered about the room "just looking at Grandma's things."

Near Grandma's chair was a tall wicker washbasket. In its lower compartment I knew were stockings to darn and clothes to mend, but in the upper basket, on a pile of bright quilt blocks, lay Grandma's silver thimble—all open at the end! Grandma said she was taught to hold her hand so that she pushed her needle through the cloth with the side of her finger instead of the end. To me that shining bit of silver was a part of Grandma, more than anything else in the room, and I loved to look at it.

I also never grew tired of looking at a group of pictures on the wall in oval walnut frames. Those bewhiskered gentlemen and the ladies in tight bodices and full skirts had been Grandma's and Grandpa's relatives long ago. And the whatnot!—shelf after shelf of interesting things. A little pitcher for holding matches, made of red glass, had something like sandpaper along the side to scratch them on. It was rough but it sparkled with all kinds of colors.

Then there were several mementoes that people had brought Grandmother from their travels. For instance, I could hold the conch shell up to my ear and hear the roar of the ocean!—But what caught my fancy most was a glass dome of stuffed birds that stood on Grandma's mahogany table. Grandmother had always kept a bird, and whenever one died she had it mounted and put into this case. There was Dick, her first canary, and the red bird—he was beautiful! There were two mockingbirds who would never sing here in Iowa. I looked at them sorrowfully; the poor birds must have been very homesick!

Preface

On the table lay the stereopticon with a pile of views beside it and the plush-covered photograph album.

When Grandma came into the room to see me, she was usually tying her white starched apron that had homemade knitted lace at the bottom. I loved this Grandma with her auburn hair lightly streaked with white, combed into a knot on top of her head behind a little pompadour, and her green-brown eyes kindling with affection as she gave me a pat on the head.

When she moved across the room to settle her plump, genial self in the lower rocker by the window, I followed eagerly and found my usual place on a footstool that Grandma had made long ago of tin cans covered with ingrain carpet.

Now when Grandma picked up her glasses and some quilt blocks, she looked down at me and smiled, and I knew that everything was ready for a story. Many a happy hour I spent listening to stories of her early days—real pioneer stories—the very stories you will find in this book.

IOWA HANNAH

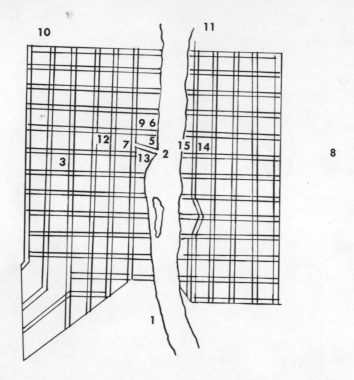

10   11

9 6
12   7   5   15   14   8
3   13   2

1

WATERLOO, IOWA 1854

Original Plat Facsimile

1. ANTHONY BAKER CABIN
2. BRIDGE
3. WEST SIDE SCHOOL
4. CIRCUS GROUNDS
5. EGGER'S SAWMILL
6. GEORGE HANNA'S HOME
7. RAYMOND'S GROCERY STORE
8. RAILROAD SHOPS
9. FANCHER'S STORE
10. THE MULLAN CABIN
11. THE VIRDEN CABIN
12. CHURCH
13. COUCH'S FLOUR MILL
14. THOMPSON'S DRYGOODS STORE
15. CEDAR MILL

1

The Bakers Pioneer to Iowa

ONE Sunday afternoon, in July in the year 1853, the Anthony Baker family went to visit their neighbors, the Hallocks. They lived not far from the Bakers in southern Illinois, near the town of Alton. Mr. Hallock was in bed with rheumatism and worrying about a farm—only he didn't call it a farm. He called it a government patent.

"I was out there in Iowa early this year," Mr. Hallock told Father Baker, "and looked the country over. I picked out a piece of land and entered it at the land office at Dubuque the twenty-fifth of February. It's a hundred and sixty acres lying along the west bank of the Red Cedar

17

River. Near the ford called Prairie Rapids Crossing there's a little settlement of about twenty families—"

"Plenty of Indians out there, aren't there?" interrupted Father Baker.

"Yes, there are," said Mr. Hallock, "but they let the settlers alone pretty much except to come begging at their doors occasionally." Then he went on to say that it was his opinion that a lot of people from Illinois and still farther east would be going there in the spring and that all the trails would be full of prairie schooners.

"Don't you hate to leave southern Illinois?" asked Father Baker. "You have so many friends here."

"Well, yes, in a way," Mr. Hallock answered thoughtfully, "except I believe I can do better out there. The country is just as fertile as here, but," he added disconsolately, "I'm afraid I'm going to lose that land. They put a six months' time limit on settling on it, and this leg of mine will hardly let me turn over in bed. I'll never be able to get my family out there before the time is up."

After the two men talked and talked for several hours Mr. Hallock made a proposition to Father Baker.

"If you'll go ahead out there," he said, "and hold the land till I can come, I'll give you half of it."

"By Jove, that's a fair offer!" Father Baker exclaimed, and in a few days he and his family were on the trail west. Hannah, his eldest daughter, drove the canvas-covered wagon in which rode her mother and the four younger children, with the few household goods they could carry. Father Baker followed on horseback, driving forty head of

18

cattle that jogged along behind the wagon at their own gait.

They kept house in the wagon; slept there, too—all except Father. He rolled up in a big buffalo robe under the wagon where he could keep an eye on the cattle and horses and replenish the fire to keep the wolves away. He was a tall, powerfully built man who could stand a lot of hardship.

For a couple of weeks in Illinois the trail was wide and well beaten and the land gently rolling, just the kind of land they were accustomed to. After a month of traveling, though, the trail began to be rougher. One day the white-topped schooner with the pails and kettles, the lantern and the churn tied underneath, and the big plow fastened on the back, jolted along up a narrow, stony trail. Deep ravines sloped down between the wooded hills. Keeping a firm grip on the lines to hold the tired horses to the trail, Hannah urged them to the crest of the hill. The cattle meandered along behind the wagon, grabbing bites of the tall blue-joint grass along the way.

When the schooner reached the top of the ridge, Hannah pulled the horses to a halt. Never had she seen such a view as that which spread out before her.

"Come," she called to her mother, who was lying inside the wagon on a bed beside little three-year-old Julia. "Oh, come, see what a beautiful view!" In the distance the bluffs on the Iowa side of the Mississippi stood out purple against the western sky.

"I want to camp here!" Hannah continued. "I want to look at those beautiful hills all evening. See that one over there that stands out so much higher than the others?"

"Call to your pa," replied her mother, while little Julia scrambled off the bed. "Tell him I'm tired of the jolting. Ask him can't we stop here and not make the descent till morning."

So they made a fire near a fallen log. Father drove the cattle to a stream in the ravine nearby, where they could drink and graze. He turned them over to the children to herd while he picked the feathers off a wild turkey he had shot that afternoon. When it was cleaned, he fastened it on spits—long, pointed rods put into each side of the fowl—and then suspended it over the fire with poles.

Mother stirred up some corn bread and baked it in the spider, a long-handled frying pan with legs, which she set over the coals.

While they ate their supper, the crickets chirped in the tall grass. Farther off an owl hooted in the woods. The August sun turned to a ball of gold, gradually sinking behind the distant wooded heights. Hannah could not stop talking about the beauty of the view. She wanted to stay right there.

"We can't live on scenery, Sis," her father laughed. "We've got to get to that good Iowa farm land of Mr. Hallock's."

"It's still such a long way," Mother complained. "We don't go far in a day, do we?"

"Oh, we must have made twelve miles today," Father answered cheerfully. "It was upgrade most of the way. And, of course, the cattle are tired and don't drive as fast as they did the first few days on the road."

"Maybe the land's not worth the journey, Anthony." Mother was tired. She was a frail little woman.

"Now, Sarah Ann, don't you get discouraged." Father had such a big voice that it must have echoed back from the woods. "We're getting near Dubuque even if we can't see the river yet. We'll likely cross the Mississippi tomorrow," he went on hopefully, "and see what Iowa looks like." He patted Mother's hand. "We'll get our cabin built before snow flies and then you'll be glad you came." His enthusiasm cheered them all.

Next day, just as Father had predicted, they reached the ferry landing where they would cross the Mississippi on a big flat boat. When they drove the prairie schooner onto the ferry, Hannah was delighted. "Isn't this fun?" she asked the younger children. They nodded, but out in the middle of the stream the strong current frightened them. It slewed the boat around. Would they make the other side? Nobody talked for a little while. Finally they did reach the other landing, where they had to wait quite a long time for the ferry to go back for Father and the cattle.

At last they were in Iowa where their new home was to be. When they had started on the trail again, they saw that many little villages had sprung up along the river. Travel through the hills was difficult, until after a day or two, the country began to flatten out. It was quite well settled, too, but as they went farther west they had to cross some wet swamps and small creeks that were wild with dense growth. The team had a hard time pulling the heavy wagon.

23

"Keep going," Hannah's father told her when they came to a deep muddy place. "Don't let the horses stop. You'll come through all right." And they did—except once, when the wheels sank deep in a mudhole. It seemed they might be stuck there forever, but Father pulled out his long-handled shovel and in half a day he had them out. A strong man, Father Baker.

They had traveled about twenty-five miles west of Dubuque when they came to a little settlement of log cabins clustered on the open prairie—a village called Dyersville. Since it was late afternoon, and there was a good camping place nearby, they stopped for the night. They cared for the cattle and horses, and ate their evening meal. While they were sitting around resting in the twilight, Father said he thought he'd walk back to the little log inn. He had noticed it as they came through the settlement. Perhaps he could get some information about the condition of the trail farther west.

He found the innkeeper very friendly. After he gave Father the information he wanted about the trail, he began telling about the experience he had had that very afternoon, some two hours before the stagecoach was due to come in at his hotel to pick up the mail, as it did twice a week.

"About one o'clock," said the innkeeper, "a man suddenly appeared in the doorway there and said he was a mail agent and wanted the mail. I was suspicious of him.

" 'I'm responsible for that mail, sir,' says I, 'and unless you can prove you're a mail agent, I'm not a-goin' to give it to you.' With that he whips out a knife—and believe me, it was a long one!

"I was helpless; but my wife saved me! Quick as a wink she jumped in front of me. That seemed to unnerve the robber, and he backed out and fled—the rapscallion!"

When Father returned from the inn he said nothing to Mother about the innkeeper's story, but slept with an ear alert for any intruder. He knew his dog would warn him, and he didn't want his wife having to risk her life to save his!

Early the next morning he and his family broke camp and were again on their journey. After traveling another twenty-five miles in three days, they came to the Maquoketa River. It looked deep and the banks were steep. Father left the cattle and rode his horse up to the wagon.

"Don't be afraid, Hannah," he said. "There're wagon tracks going into the water where others have driven across. Just guide the horses enough so that you aim for the other side where the wagon tracks come up out of the water."

Hannah urged the horses in. Halfway across the water came up higher on the wheels than it had at any time before when they had forded a stream. The children weren't scared because they were watching Father swimming the cattle across. The animals kept scattering, and he had to swim his horse out first one way and then another to bring them back. It was an exciting scene. Each cow meant dollars and cents to them, but even so they wished their father wouldn't risk his life trying to save them. Hannah got the team and the wagon across and Mr. Baker got the cattle. There was a happy reunion on the other side.

Again at the Wapsipinicon, twenty-five miles farther on, there was no bridge or ferry, but this river was shallower and easier to ford. One night their camping place was Pilot's Grove. Everyone cheered up. They knew they were nearing their destination now.

The Anthony Bakers had been five weeks on the way before they arrived just at dusk along the east side of the Red Cedar River and found the ford called Prairie Rapids Crossing. A long sand bar extended into the clear river. There was the little settlement on the other side, just as Mr. Hallock had described it to them. The log cabins, with their dark wisps of smoke curling up from the chimneys, looked very inviting.

Suddenly, though, Mother cried in dismay. "Anthony! Anthony! Look at the Indians over there on the riverbank!" Sure enough, there were clusters of them starting their campfires on the shore. "Let's not ford over there tonight!"

But Hannah was made of stronger stuff. "Oh, yes, Ma, let's go across. Don't be afraid," she encouraged her mother. "I'm hungry, and it seems like supper is cooking in those four cabins. But look, there's one house that doesn't have any smoke coming out of the chimney!"

Father rode up and clapped Hannah on the back for her

courage. She was a "clipper" he said. That meant she wasn't afraid of anything. After much debate, however, Mother Baker won out and they decided to camp where they were for the night, with the wide river flowing between them and the Indians.

2

Building the Log Cabin

EVERYONE was up early the next morning, peering anxiously at the opposite shore as soon as light broke through. There were no Indians in sight! "Let's get going before they come back!" cried Hannah, and urged her team into the water. The river was high and the water swirled around the prairie schooner, but Hannah succeeded in keeping the horses on the smooth rock floor of the ford. Behind her, Father had trouble getting the cattle across. They kept spreading out as they had before. Finally, the last cow scrambled up on the shore. By this time quite a few people were down at the water's edge to welcome them.

Mother and the children were invited into Mr. George Hanna's cabin near the riverbank. Other cabins stood farther back on higher ground. The men gathered around Father, wanting to know where he came from and all about the journey.

"Quite a nice settlement you have," Father said. "Mostly log houses, but you have one little frame house, I see. Where did you get the lumber for that?"

"Oh, that's my house," a settler replied. "I hauled the sawed boards from a mill farther up the river at Sturges Falls. There's nobody living in it yet. I built it for my brother, but he's decided not to come till spring. Say, you could live in it this winter if you'd like to!"

"Well, now, you don't say so?" Father thought he was the luckiest man in the world. It didn't take him long to stride over to Mr. Hanna's to tell Mother. She agreed right away, and the children clapped their hands. Their long, hard journey was over!

After they had moved their belongings out of the prairie schooner and were well settled in the little house, Father did some "breaking" on his and Mr. Hallock's land while the weather was fine. Then he could plant sod corn in the spring.

It was very quiet out on the prairie that fall. Father heard only the chirp of the crickets and the song of the birds. The green grass stretched away as far as he could see. Sometimes the clouds cast beautiful shadows on the grass, making it different shades of green. Often a wild turkey sprang up ahead of the plow, frightened out of its nest in the tall grass.

As the days passed by and the early frosts came, the beautiful green of the prairie turned brown. Father often stopped at the end of a furrow to rest his horses and file the point of his plow. Now, he decided, was about time to stop plowing and begin cutting the trees for lumber for his cabin. He wanted to have enough cut to build it in the early spring.

One day he drove the team up the river toward Sturges Falls to his timber claim and began picking out the tallest and straightest trees. All winter he worked, chopping down the trees with his wide broadax. Near the ends of each log he cut notches so that the logs would fit together when the cabin was built. His hard work kept him from getting cold, yet some days his lunch would have frozen if he hadn't built a little fire to keep it warm. He was glad to have the fire to sit by while he ate.

Every member of the family, young and old, had work to do. They must prepare for the long Iowa winter. Hannah helped with the cooking and preserving. The younger girls took turns watching over baby Harlan. Most of the food came from other families in the settlement because it would be several months before the Bakers could harvest anything. "How kind and generous these new Iowa neighbors are," thought Hannah.

At night Hannah and the younger children could see their father's team coming down the river on the ice with

Father sitting on the sled. While he piled the logs by a nice clear spring along the river, they hopped around, chattering to him or listening to the bright water that bubbled up out of the ground and ran down to the river. This lively two-foot spring was near the place where Father would build the cabin early that year.

Finally, the winter was over and spring came to Iowa. One day in May all the men of the settlement came together for a "house raising." They began by laying down two logs as far apart as the house was to be wide. Then they placed two logs, one at each end. As they laid the logs, a man stood at each corner to fit them together with the notches that Father had cut near the ends. It was a large cabin for those days, for Father had five children: Hannah, Rosetta, Cornelia, Julia, and baby Harlan.

When the house was high enough to start the roof, they laid smaller logs across for the ceiling of the downstairs rooms. Next, the gable ends were built up for the roof to rest on.

Father had the clapboards all ready when the roof was finished. Clapboards were heavy shingles hewn out of logs —three or four feet long—which were laid over the smaller logs used for the rafters of the roof. Because the early settlers had no nails, they set poles across to hold the clapboard shingles in place and fastened the poles down with wooden pegs. Next they cut the openings—a window and a door.

By the end of one day's work the cabin was up, but not all ready to move into. There were still many things to be done, things Hannah and the other children could help Father do. The cracks between the logs must be filled with little pieces of wood—"chinked," they called it—and the chinking had to be "daubed" over with clay from the river-bank to keep out the wind and cold of winter.

Besides the "chink, chinking" and the "daub, daubing" they did to help Father, the children had lots of fun running about the prairie, hunting big rounded rocks to make the fireplace. Often the children drew funny faces on the stones with a charred stick. They shouted with laughter at the faces that smiled back at them.

By the time the cabin had a roof on and the chimney built, Mother was very anxious to move in. The people from the east in whose house they were living would be coming soon. She was willing to live on a dirt floor until winter when Father would have time to lay a "puncheon" floor. It would be made of split logs smoothed off with the split side for the floor.

What comfort it would be to have a wooden floor! Meanwhile, it was wonderful to have a place of their own. Perhaps in a few more weeks their friends, the Hallocks, would arrive. Hannah hoped so. She was beginning to miss her friends in Illinois.

3

An Evening in the Log Cabin

HANNAH loved to spin. In the evening, now that their cabin was built, she would draw the big spinning wheel out into the middle of the room near the fireplace. How pretty she looked as she moved gracefully backward and forward in front of the glowing flames. Her hair was auburn, and the warm color blended with the butternut brown of her full skirt.

On the platform of the spinning wheel lay a pile of little rolls of carded wool about the size of a woman's finger. Picking up one of the rolls, Hannah pulled out a few fibers from one end and attached them to the point of the

35

spindle, a rod on which the yarn would be wound. With her left hand she caught hold of the little roll of wool at the exact distance from the spindle to make one "drawing" of yarn, and started the wheel by striking the spokes with a little stick. The turning wheel set the spindle to turning, twisting the fibers into a thread of yarn.

Hannah stepped quickly backward, one step, two steps, three steps, and the spindle drew the thread longer still, twisting it more firmly. Lifting high her left hand, which held the long thread of yarn, she ran quickly forward three steps and allowed the yarn to wind itself around the rapidly moving spindle, making one "drawing" of yarn.

Before the drawing was complete, Hannah held onto a little remnant of the yarn with her thumb and finger. She picked up another roll of the carded wool from the platform of the wheel, and the roll was caught to the little remnant.

Again and again she repeated the process of drawing and joining.

Soothed by the hum of the spinning wheel, baby Harlan, in the big bed in the corner of the room, had gone to sleep with little Julia beside him.

At the "puncheon" table Rosetta and Cornelia were doing their "sums" in preparation for school in the little log schoolhouse the next day.

Father had made the dinner table of logs. The top was split logs and the legs were round logs. It was strong and large. Not only did the family eat at it, but Mother prepared all the food there. And it served as study table, too.

An Evening in the Log Cabin

Tonight Mother was tired. She had been making soap today. For a long time she had been saving the grease from cooking. Wood ashes from the fireplace furnished the lye. Every day for a week she had poured water into the top of a barrel of ashes that stood outside the cabin door. The water seeped down through the ashes and out some holes in the bottom of the barrel into a wooden pail. This made the lye.

To be sure the lye was strong enough, Mother tested it with an egg. She dropped the egg into a pailful of the lye water. If the egg floated, the lye was strong enough. Today it didn't, so she poured the lye water through some fresh ashes. She did it several times, until at last she saw the egg floating just under the surface of the water, with a round spot about the size of a five-cent piece showing above the water. Now she had strong lye to boil with the grease in a big outdoor kettle over an open fire. Carefully she stirred it round and round in one direction with a wooden paddle on the end of a long stick. By and by the soap was done; funny soap, for it looked like thick jelly! If was "soft soap" and was very strong. Mother was glad to have finished her task.

The evening went quickly, until Mother reminded the girls that it was time to set the table for breakfast. In their red dresses they went back and forth across the room getting the dishes from the clapboard shelf which served as a cupboard. They turned the plates upside down over the bone-handled knives and forks of steel. The plates were heavy, for they were ironstone china.

The fire burned down soon after supper and was then

ready to be banked for the night. The burned-down candles no longer gave enough light to work by. Father put away the ax handle he had been carving. Mother opened the big family Bible and read a chapter while they all sat before the fire listening. Then Father Baker gave the evening prayer: "Almighty God, we thank Thee for rest and health; for work to do, and strength to do it. Forgive us of our sins. Protect us through the night. Guide us through the day to come. In His name we ask Thy blessing. Amen."

Now Father went to the mantelshelf to wind the precious clock they had brought with them in the covered wagon. That done, he crossed the room, took down the bootjack from its peg on the wall, and catching first one heel and then the other in its helpful U-shaped end, he removed his heavy boots. These he took time to grease before going to bed.

Baby Harlan was already asleep in his cradle. As soon as Father had pulled out the black walnut trundle bed, Mother tucked in the two little girls, Cornelia and the sleeping Julia. The bed had a little railing around the sides and ends. It was so low that during the day it was rolled on its casters out of sight under the one-legged bed in the corner of the room, so called because the head and one side were fastened into the log walls which made the corner and the only leg needed was for the end of the bed that stuck out into the room. The mattress was a tick stuffed with cornhusks. It was lumpy.

While the younger girls were getting settled in their

trundle bed, Hannah and Rosetta climbed the ladder to the loft. Soon their heads disappeared through the square hole at the top of the ladder. Two husk mattresses covered the floor of the loft. Hannah and Rosetta lay down on these and spread a goose-down quilt over themselves. Their voices murmured a while until they dozed off to sleep, and the house was still.

4

The Hallocks Arrive

"I THINK it's the Hallocks coming," Hannah announced excitedly one morning, as she rushed into the cabin. "They're fording the river now, and they're swimming a lot of cattle across."

"Oh, our old neighbors!" exclaimed Mother, who was peeling potatoes for the stew boiling in the big iron kettle. This hung on the crane in the fireplace.

Mother ran out of the cabin. She had known the Hallocks were coming soon, because she had received a letter from them, but she hadn't expected them for a few days.

As she left, Mother called out to Hannah to peel a generous amount of potatoes for the stew, and to stir up a big mess of corn bread.

When Mother brought Mrs. Hallock and her children into the cabin, Mrs. Hallock was saying that she loved Iowa already, the song of the meadowlark, the fragrance of the wild plum blossoms, and the wide, rolling prairie, gay with millions of prairie lilies, yellow cowslips, and red and purple phlox.

"It's so much more beautiful than I thought it would be," she confessed.

"Yes," agreed Mother, "I'm glad you came in May and could see the prairie in its spring dress. It is so lovely! But they tell me that the coarse prairie grass is always full of wild flowers."

"How about the journey?" asked Hannah as Mr. Hallock and Father came in. "Did you get stuck in a mudhole the way we did?"

"No, but it was a hard trip," Mr. Hallock answered. "I thought it would never end. Father and I were just talking about how fine it would be to have a railroad to bring people out here."

"Yes, and we'll have one in ten years," Father predicted.

Mr. Hallock couldn't believe that. They argued mildly for a while until Father told them he had received their letter only last week when Greenbury Luck, the mail rider, came in with the mail.

"Do they still put the letters in the teapot just inside the door of Charlie Mullan's cabin? That's the way they did last year when I was here and picked out my land." Mr. Hallock laughed.

"Yes," replied Father Baker, "makes it handy, too. No need to bother the postmaster when he's about his work. Just reach in and help yourself."

The young ones were getting restless standing around, so Mother asked Rosetta and Cornelia to take all the children and pick some wild strawberries for dinner.

When they were gone she said proudly, "We've got a school started here now. The men got together and put up a log schoolhouse, and Eliza May is the teacher. There're not many children, but we're glad to have a school for them so we don't have to teach them at home."

"Another thing we're proud of is the ferry," Father chimed in. "You didn't cross on it but you could have. Samuel May built the boat and he crosses upstream, about half a mile from here. The thing we need now is a sawmill, and we think we're going to get it."

"Have to have a dam built first to give you power," warned Mr. Hallock.

"George Hanna has just sold the site for a mill to James Eggers for only a dollar, providing he will build a sawmill there. Eggers says he's going to start the dam and the mill right away."

"Then they'll have a town here for sure!" Mr. Hallock prophesied. "I reckon 1854's going to be the 'birthday' year for Prairie Rapids. Only it's going to be called Water-

44

loo, Iowa, in the plat. Charlie Mullan, the postmaster, has already sent that name in to the Post Office Department."

"Well, he and George Hanna have worked hard to get a town started. George says he'll donate the land to anyone who will start a shop or store here. The county is settling up. There's over three hundred here now. I don't know whether a town will grow or not, but I hope so."

Mr. Hallock's face grew sober. "Wish I had the logs out for my cabin. It's a long, tiresome task."

"Oh, don't worry. We have all winter to get that done," said Father encouragingly, "and in the meantime, Mr. Eggers has a cabin you can live in."

"We have a doctor here now." Mother Baker was full of good news. "He came last fall. We're thankful for that. Some of the settlers here had ague bad since they broke up the prairie sod. Are you all over your rheumatism, Mr. Hallock?"

"Oh, it doesn't bother me much now that I carry a buckeye in my pocket."

"A buckeye?" Mother didn't see the connection.

"Yes, it's a cousin to the horse chestnut. One of the men I met on the way told me he carries a potato; showed it to me. It was as hard as a rock, but he said he never had rheumatism while he carried it."

"Well, they say Nature furnishes a remedy for every ill," Mother answered agreeably. "We use lots of boneset tea." And she got up to help Hannah with the dinner.

Father went on with the conversation. "What we need

here now is the sawmill, and a flour mill, too, Louis, so we won't have to haul our wheat sixty miles to be ground into flour."

"Yes," Mother was pulling the Dutch oven from under the hot coals on the hearth, "I've learned to use corn meal in a dozen ways, and if we ever get a flour mill I never want to see any more corn meal!"

"I'm afraid that'll be a long time yet," said Mrs. Hallock. "Anyway, the corn bread certainly smells good."

The children came back with a pail of strawberries, and soon two big bowls of the ripe red fruit glowed on the long puncheon table. That and the appetizing aroma of venison stew made everyone hungry.

There were so many seated around the table there weren't enough seats for all the children, and they had to stand. After Father had asked the blessing, he began telling Mr. Hallock that last fall Charles Mullan had done the surveying and then he and George Hanna and John Brooks made a little plat or map of the west side.

"East side ought to be platted, too," Mr. Hallock asserted. "Now that they've got the ferry, it's bound to settle up over there. Won't be wolves here much longer, or Indians going up and down the river, either." Warm food seemed to make Mr. Hallock more cheerful.

"I don't know about that. Some children on the prairie were chased half a mile by a pack of hungry wolves last winter," said Mother, "but they had a head start and managed to reach the cabin in safety. The wolves dug a hole under the side of the cabin trying to get in! Lucky

46

their parents got back in time to save them. My! how I hate to hear those critters howl at night."

"Are you afraid of Indians, Sarah?" Mr. Hallock asked.

"No, I'm not afraid any more. The first night we camped on the east side of the river I was afraid, even though I pretended I wasn't. I've seen so many of them since. Last fall a hundred or more camped in the timber west of here for weeks, hunting and trapping in the woods there. The squaws often came to the house to beg."

"I hate to think of any moccasined feet sneaking around my cabin," said Mrs. Hallock.

"They really are quite friendly," Mother assured her, "if you treat them well."

After dinner Father took Mr. Hallock out to see the breaking he had done and the patch of sod corn he had planted. They talked about dividing the land to give Father half of it because he had come on ahead so that Mr. Hallock wouldn't lose it.

When Mr. Hallock said he would rather have the part that lay higher and back from the river, Father said that such a division suited him exactly. Father had an idea that there were quarries of building stone not far from where he had built his cabin. He wanted to develop them, he said, for people would be needing stone for foundations when they began to build houses of lumber.

After a while Father and Mr. Hallock went uptown to see the new schoolhouse and the one store. They had a long talk with Mr. George Hanna, who said that Mr. Eggers certainly would start the dam soon.

What Mr. Hallock laughingly said about 1854 being the birthday year really came true. On June 24 a plat (a map) of the small town was made and recorded. There were just a handful of cabins scattered about. The rest were farther out on the prairie, but others would be built, and the town would surely grow.

5

The Circuit Rider

HANNAH was scrubbing the puncheon table. A fire of hickory logs burned in the big fireplace, and a turkey, all nicely dressed, hung over the fire. As the turkey roasted to a delicious brown, the fat dripped down into a pan set in the ashes to catch it. Some corn bread was baking in a covered iron pan buried in the live coals. The cabin was full of mouth-watering smells.

All of this preparation was for a special occasion. The circuit rider—a traveling preacher—was coming to dinner. Traveling preachers rode horseback all over the wide prairie plains, following the Indian trails to the various settlements.

It was a great event to have the circuit rider come. The children had got some extra scrubbing behind the ears last night when Mother bathed them in the little wooden tub placed in front of the fireplace. The very best quilts had been taken out of the chest and spread over the beds this morning.

When Hannah had finished cleaning the puncheon table she spread it with a homemade woven cloth. Then she polished up the pewter spoons. Pewter was made of tin, copper, and lead, and was cheaper than silver.

During the winter Father had cut down a small tree and made some stools—people called them puncheon stools because, like the floors, the split side of the log was turned up for the seat part of the stools. Everyone had felt very proud of the ones Father had made when he brought them into the cabin.

The good circuit rider arrived soon after Hannah had finished setting the table. He was cold and hungry after his long horseback ride and had little to say at first, but the dinner was warm and good, and soon the conversation started up as the children lost their shyness. Brother James had many interesting stories to tell of his experiences riding the circuit. One winter he used an old rocking chair for a sled to carry supplies.

The Bakers told him that church services would be held that evening in the schoolhouse. The Methodists, the Presbyterians, and the Baptists had to share the little log cabin which the men of the settlement had built for a schoolhouse, so there was a preaching service in the morning, the afternoon, and the evening, to accommodate the different faiths. Now about three hundred people lived in the county and three churches had been organized already!

That evening, when the Bakers and the circuit rider arrived for church, Mother and the children sat on one side of the room with the women. Father sat on the other side with the men. Of course they took baby Harlan to church, too. People didn't stay home because babies might cry during the meeting. If the preacher couldn't be heard above the babies, he wasn't considered much good.

There were no lamps in the schoolhouse, so the Bakers brought some candles along. These Father placed on the wide window sills among the other candles already there. They also brought their little hymnbook which had only the words, no notes of music. Good church men and women were supposed to know their hymn music. The book was very small, only about three inches long and two inches wide. The print was very fine, but because the book was thick, it had many hymns in it. Later the churches had melodeons, but in this little log schoolhouse there was no musical instrument. The congregation made up for it by singing loudly.

The Bakers could have had a violin in their church, for Dr. McKinley, the first doctor in the community, played one. He was never invited to do so, however. Violins were not used in churches in those days. The "fiddle" was fit only for dancing, and dancing was forbidden by the church.

As the service started, the song leader stood up to "line off" the words of the hymn for the benefit of those who had no books. He read the lines

> O for a thousand tongues to sing
> My great Redeemer's praise!

Then he pitched the tune by means of a tuning fork. This was called "lifting the tune."

After they had sung the first two lines, the leader "lined off" the next two. Hannah found it hard to follow the tune with so many interruptions. Still, the song leader read off the lines quite quickly and rhythmically, and everyone at least got the thought of the hymn that way.

The tunes were handed down. There were "Rock of Ages" and "Old Hundred." Also, every song leader knew a few tunes which he might have learned at singing school, and the church people learned them by rote from the leader. There were only a few people capable of leading, and the singing was good or bad, depending on the leader. In fact, the bad singing in some churches and the many discussions which would arise as to just how the tune went were the main reasons why melodeons were finally used in churches. Even so, many people thought they were instruments of the devil!

This evening, when the Bakers went to church in the log schoolhouse, the minister preached a rousing missionary sermon. As the little oblong contribution boxes on their long handles were held out in front of every person, Hannah saw a young bride take off her earrings and drop them into the box instead of money. "Probably she doesn't have as much money as she would like to give," Hannah thought, but she was surprised just the same. The early churches were very earnest about missionary work. Their members tried to carry out Christ's command to "go into all the world and preach the gospel," and they gave as much as they could to this end.

6

A Pioneer Wedding

IT was the eleventh of July, and Eliza, Mr. and Mrs.
May's daughter, and Isaac Virden were to be married at
last! Eliza was the first schoolteacher in the log cabin
schoolhouse. She and Isaac had met when the circuit rider
held services in the Virden home. That was about a year
ago. It was a case of love at first sight, but getting married wasn't so easy in pioneer times. Young people could
never tell what would happen to upset their plans.

Shortly after they had decided on a day in June, all the
young men were called out to put down an Indian uprising
farther north. The settlement was in a commotion. Every-

one was concerned about the Indians, but Eliza's little sister, Anna, could talk of nothing but her sister's marriage.

"Just think!" she said to one of her little schoolmates. "It'll be the first wedding in Waterloo!"

"Why, no," said one of the other girls. "Don't you remember that Isaac's sister Elizabeth and Nelson Fancher were married a few weeks ago?"

"Oh, their wedding doesn't count," said Anna, "because they were married in the Virden home, quite a ways from the settlement—a farm home. My sister is going to be married in town."

As the day for Eliza's wedding approached, Anna thought she had a wonderful idea. She went about the neighborhood inviting everyone to the wedding! Eliza found it out just in time.

"What made you think we could have the wedding with Isaac gone to fight the Indians, you crazy girl?" she asked.

"Why, he'll surely come back for the day of his own wedding, won't he?"

"He may never come back!" Eliza wailed. "How do we know he isn't scalped by this time! Now you go right back and tell all those people not to come!" And that's what the confused little sister had to do.

At last, however, Isaac was safe home again. The invitations were given out, this time for the afternoon of July 11. That was in 1854, the year after Father Baker's folks came to Waterloo.

The day before the wedding Mother Baker went over to the Mays' to help with the baking.

"This stove of yours is surely a comfort," said Mother. "Cooking on it is so much easier than cooking in a fireplace. I hope that sometime soon Anthony can bring out a stove for me after he takes a load of wheat to Dubuque."

"That stove is a delight to me every day of my life," replied Mrs. May proudly.

The women had just finished the last cake when Mr. May came home and told his daughter he was sure the circuit-riding minister, Brother Ingam, could not reach Waterloo in time for the wedding because of the high water. She and Isaac had better arrange to be married by Judge Pratt.

Poor Eliza was nearly in despair. What else was going to happen! Did ever a bride have so many disappointments! She went over to the corner of the one-room cabin and climbed the rude ladder that led to the upper floor. Here, on one of the several beds in the long loft, lay her beautiful wedding dress. How many hours she had spent making it! She looked down at it with a mixture of pride and despair. She had had quite a time getting it. There was no sewing machine nearby in those days, but Eliza's mother had brought yards of dress material from Indiana when she came to Iowa in the covered wagon, and Eliza's nimble fingers had made every single garment for her wedding trousseau. Rows of narrow tucks ornamented the ruffles on the bottom of her white muslin petticoat. The bosom of her chemise (a long, homemade underskirt or slip) was made of pieces of solid tucking set together with insertion of hand-knit lace.

56

The wedding dress itself was beautiful. All around the skirt and the overskirt were diamond-shaped medallions of fine needlework with the cloth underneath cut away—cut work they call it now. It had taken Eliza weeks and weeks to finish it.

Now the girl held the dress up to her slim figure and looked into the little mirror that hung on a nail at the end of the loft.

"I had wanted so much to be married by the minister, Brother Ingam," she complained to herself. Then she thought of the letter she had received yesterday from her old chum back in Indiana, who had been a June bride.

"I was to be a June bride, too," thought Eliza woefully, "but the Indians spoiled that! And now I can't even be married by a minister!"

That evening, however, when she and Isaac talked it over, she felt more cheerful. They decided that they might just as well accept life as it came in this new country and not let disappointments spoil things for them.

On the eventful day of the wedding Isaac's people were the first to arrive. Mrs. Virden laid her bonnet on the bed built into a corner of the room. Next came the newlyweds, the Fanchers. Their cabin was at Elk Run down the river, and their talk was all about the high water near their recently built home.

The Browns, who had been old friends of the Mays in Numa, Indiana, came driving all the way from Independence, Iowa, twenty-five miles away. Twenty-five miles with work horses was quite a trip. After they arrived on the east bank of the river, they were ferried across on Mr. May's ferry.

Next came the Miers, who had a sawmill at the east end of the dam. They thought Brother Ingam might still get back in time. His horse could swim any stream, they said, no matter how swollen.

The time came for the ceremony, however, and he had not arrived. Eliza and Isaac stood up before the wide fireplace. Judge Pratt took his place before the young people and read the sacred covenant. Eliza promised to love, honor, and obey. Isaac promised to love, honor, and protect. They didn't know it at the time, but they were to keep these promises as long as they both lived.

Before the ceremony the table was already set for the wedding feast. Mother Baker was to help serve the wedding supper, so she hurried off behind the calico curtains that hung around one corner of the room to make a kitchen.

They had a lovely meal, but all the guests had to leave early, for each family had work that must be done before nightfall. So, shortly after the cake was served and the congratulations offered, family by family they departed—all except the Browns. Mother Baker had invited them to spend the night at their cabin because it was too late to make the long drive to Independence.

Evening was coming on and they were sitting around, chatting about the events of the day, when the Mays were startled by the sudden noise of rifle fire in the distance. Their first thought was "Indians," but as the noisemakers came closer, they heard bells and tin pans. In a short time the cabin was entirely surrounded by a charivari party. They had come to celebrate the wedding! After they had finished their noisy celebration, they were invited into the cabin for some wedding cake.

Neighbors who were living some distance away and not concerned with the wedding naturally thought of Indians, too, after the recent scare. Several families who had heard the rifle shots and the shouting hitched their horses to their wagons and left the settlement in a great hurry. As people along the road heard the running horses and ran out of their cabins, the escaping families shouted out, "Run for your lives! The Indians are upon us!"

Warned in this way, one family started for the river to hide in the bulrushes because they thought the Indians would follow the trail south. All night they hid there. At sunrise they saw a settler come out of his cabin not far away to start the day's work. An hour or two later the farmer's wife came out and hung out the washing. This display of courage so steadied the nerves of the frightened family hiding in the bushes that they returned to the settlement, although they felt sure they would find all the inhabitants massacred by the Indians. They were certainly surprised when they heard later the true cause of the Indian raid scare!

7

The Old Mills

ONE small sawmill was built by Mr. Samuel May shortly
after the Bakers arrived. It was very slow, for it operated
by horsepower and could not supply the demand for lumber. During the summer of 1855 James Eggers built a dam
of logs and brush across the river with the help of the men
of the settlement. Father Baker said he rafted logs down
the river when the water was so high he thought every
minute would be his last.

Soon Mr. Eggers had his sawmill at the west end of the
dam completed. The wheel was under the mill, and right

at the end of the dam. The logs were floated down the river and left lying in a little bend of the west bank near the sawmill. When it was time to saw the logs, a moving chain drag with crosspieces of timber caught the end of each log and rolled it onto a carrier that hauled it up to the saw in the mill.

There was such a demand for lumber that this mill couldn't supply the needs of the settlers, and another mill was built at the other end of the dam. Two years later four sawmills were in operation.

As soon as the pioneers had sawmills to provide lumber for their homes, they found that their next great need was a flour mill to grind wheat for their bread. Mr. G. W. Couch built one in 1856. The flour mill was a very important addition to the village. It was a story and a half high and stood near the west end of the dam, a little farther downstream from the Eggers sawmill.

The millstones, about four feet across, came a long way. They were hauled by Mr. Farwell in his big lumber wagon from Iowa City. It took several yoke of oxen to pull the heavy, creaking wagon, for there were some low, muddy spots in the road. At one place he had to cut a lot of coarse prairie grass and pack the road in order to get through a stretch of mud.

The mill was started with only one set of stones, but another set was put in shortly afterward for grinding corn and feed. The wheat was ground between the two millstones. Only one millstone turned—the top one. To turn

61

it the water gate at the end of the dam was raised to allow the water to come in. Then the mill wheel set the upper millstone to turning.

The miller poured the wheat into a big hopper that was over the millstone. The wheat fell down through a hole in the upper millstone and was ground in the grooves which were cut in the stones. Outside, the mill wheel was turning round and round. Soon after the miller had lifted up a big sack of wheat and poured it into the hopper there was a crunching sound as the grain was ground between the heavy millstones. As the water poured over the wheel, the weight of it kept the big mill wheel going round and round.

After the wheat was ground between the millstones, it came out of a spout into a bin. Then it was carried upstairs by machinery to the bolting room. Here the flour was sifted through bolting cloth to separate the bran, or husk, from the flour. This silk cloth was coarse enough so that the flour would go through, but not the husk, or outside of the wheat.

One day when Hannah's younger sisters, Rosetta and Cornelia, were at the mill with Father Baker, the miller gave them enough bolting cloth to make each of them a dress. When any of the threads broke, even if it was only at one place, the cloth was useless to the miller. Many a pioneer child had a pretty dress made of bolting cloth. The creamy white silk pleased Rosetta and Cornelia. After their mother had cut out their dresses, they made their dolls dresses out of the pieces that were left.

The Old Mills

All the settlers were happy to have a flour mill at last, and it even made the Indians happy, too. After the machinery was put in, but before it was used, the Indians came to ask if they might have a dance in the mill! They were Sacs and Foxes—friendly Indians—who were camping and hunting near the village. Now the white man could grind the Indians' wheat and the braves might give their squaws fine white flour for their bread.

Wagons full of wheat were often standing all the way from Fourth to Tenth streets, waiting to unload at the mill. Many times when Hannah passed by she saw a man from the mill standing on the hub of a wheel, opening the sacks and tossing the grain up in the air with his hands to see how free of chaff and dirt it was.

After the pioneers had sawmills and a flour mill they wanted a woolen mill. Home spinning and weaving were slow, tedious work. By that time farmers were beginning to raise sheep so everyone had plenty of wool. A four-story woolen mill was built near the flour mill. It stood on solid rock, with its base four feet below the river level; and the stone walls at the bottom were six feet thick.

One day Hannah and her sisters were going through the woolen mill after it was finished. On the second floor they opened a door and stepped out on a platform. Standing there, they could see far up and down the curving shores of the beautiful tree-lined river. It was early spring, and the wild ducks were coming north. Blue-winged teal are fast fliers, and this platform was a grand place to see the swift flying blue wings, and also the larger and slower gray-green mallards coming steadily in V-formation through the sky on their way to the marshes and lakes of northern Iowa and Minnesota.

"Never have I seen such a beautiful sight," thought Hannah.

8

Hannah Goes Shopping

THE next great need of the people living in the settlement was for a bridge so that those on both sides of the river could reach the mills. During high water, fording the river was out of the question and ferrying was dangerous. So a bridge was built in this way:

Wooden piers were sunk deep in the river bed and filled with native rock. The flooring and the sides of the bridge were of rough plank. Now they could cross the river without depending on the ferry.

The east side of the river opposite the Bakers, but also

part of Waterloo, was settling up fast. There was a small hotel and a store over there now.

One day Hannah decided she wanted to go over to see the new store. "Mother, can't we buy the goods for my new school dress on the east side? I want something different from what the other girls have."

"I don't see any sense to that," Mother replied. "Our west side store has as good stuff as anybody. It's all hauled from Dubuque."

"Yes, but Mother," Hannah persisted, "I don't like three or four girls to have a dress just like mine."

"If you want to trade at the new store," Mother said, "you'll have to go alone. I'm not going to walk clear over there."

On the next Saturday Hannah started off all by herself on her shopping expedition. She felt very important as she walked up Commercial Street, past the little log cabin that had been built to accommodate men who came prospecting for land. Next, she went past Capwell's grocery on the corner of Fifth.

She stopped at the old town pump near the middle of the block. A woman who lived nearby was pumping a pail of water. Just then Ed Roebuck, a boy Hannah knew, came along. He had been hunting wild ducks up the river at Washburn's pond and had a lot of big mallards with their feet tied together.

"I see you have been duck hunting," said the woman. "I know they're mallards because they have such dark feathers. Aren't their gray-brown backs pretty?"

66

"Yes," said Hannah, "and what pretty green heads! And look, there's a green spot on each wing! What are you going to do with them?"

"I'm selling them, three for a quarter," the boy replied.

"I wish you'd go down by our house. I'm sure my mother will buy some," Hannah said.

The boy pumped a drink for each of them while Hannah held the tin cup that was fastened to the wooden pump. Just as she was leaving, a man drove up to water his team at the trough in the street. Settlers driving to the village from some distance usually needed to water their horses before returning home.

Hannah went on. Across the street was Raymonds' Grocery. She looked up at the empty sugar hogshead on top of a pole that was used as a sign for the store. It said, RAYMOND BROTHERS, SIGN OF THE SUGAR HOGSHEAD.

Merchants used to buy brown sugar in hogsheads. They were twice as big as a barrel. If an empty one was rolled out back of the store, it wasn't long before some children would be inside it, digging off the sugar and having the time of their lives.

Fourth Street was deep with mud. Hannah noticed that mud clung to the iron tires of the wagons that went by. It hung on until it nearly reached the top, then fell off in heavy chunks.

After Hannah had crossed the bridge she passed Mier's sawmill. Next came the little hotel and then Thompson's Dry Goods Store. As Hannah went in, a clerk came to wait on her. He was in shirt sleeves and was wearing his hat,

for in those days all the clerks in stores were men and they frequently wore their hats while working. Mr. Cutts, who had a grocery store, wore a plug hat in his store all the time when he waited on trade.

When Hannah told the clerk what she wanted, he went behind a counter where bolts of calico were piled up on a shelf. Hannah was delighted at such a variety. The clerk stood beside the stack of goods.

"Do you see anything there you like?" he asked, running his finger slowly down the bolts. Hannah looked critically at the few inches of each bolt of cloth that she could see.

68

"If you'd take one or two down, I believe I could tell better," she said at last, after she had screwed up her courage to ask such a favor. After a chance to see them on the counter, she chose a blue and tan stripe. The clerk wrapped the package and Hannah started for home. She walked much faster, for she could hardly wait to show her mother the pattern she had selected.

She burst in the door and eagerly held the goods out for inspection. Mother liked it. She said it was as pretty a piece of calico as she had ever seen. Then she told Hannah that she had bought some mallards and had them cleaned ready for dinner tomorrow. The boy had made a sale, just as Hannah said he would.

The next week Mother made Hannah's dress in the fashion for schoolgirls—a "princess" dress buttoned down the back, with a flounce on the bottom, elbow sleeves, pockets, and a square neck trimmed with a bit of lace. And was Hannah proud of the dress she had shopped for! Only one other girl in the whole school had one like it!

9

Sugaring Off

ABOUT three miles down the river, at Elk Run, there was a fine clump of sugar maples. Father built a shack there and spent the early spring tapping the trees and boiling sap. He made the journey back and forth in a flat-bottomed boat that he had made from rough planks the year before. Sometimes he would be there for several days at a time, sleeping in the shack at night, but usually he would come home at the end of the day. He said it was lonesome over there, listening to the plaintive song of the whippoorwill.

One day when he came home Father said, "I am ready

to sugar off now! How would you like to go back to the camp with me for a week?"

"We'd like that, Anthony," Mother replied.

Next morning everyone was busy preparing for the trip. It was only a short distance to where the boat was tied to a tree, for at that time of the year the river was over its banks. The Bakers got into the boat and started downstream.

How funny it seemed to be riding over Father's stone quarries in a boat, Hannah thought. The river looked wide —almost like a lake, but long, too, with the water flowing very fast.

"Sit still in the boat!" Father commanded. "Don't anyone stand up." He seemed very stern.

Out in the middle of the stream the current was strong and swift. It was all Father could do to keep the boat headed toward the other shore.

"Isn't this exciting!" Hannah whispered. Mother in her gray shawl and bright quilted hood had her arms around Julia and Harlan. Rosetta and Cornelia were very quiet and a little breathless.

When they reached the camp, it was just as Father had described it to them. They saw their own two horses tied to the trees near the shack. Nearby two big iron kettles hung from a pole stretched between two forked trees.

"All the trees look as if they have pipe stems sticking out of their sides!" Mother said.

"That's right," agreed Father. "There's been a good run

71

of sap this year. The frost has gone out of the ground gradually, and because the snow stayed so long, the tree trunks have kept moist."

That night they all slept in mangers instead of beds. Father had built the mangers inside the shack to store hay for the horses.

When Father lifted the younger girls, Cornelia and Julia, over the side of their manger, they snuggled down among the blankets in the soft, sweet-smelling hay. It had been grown on the hillside and was full of wild flowers. It sunk way down, and how odd it seemed with the sides of the manger so high they couldn't see out! They kept reaching up to touch the sides of the manger, listening all the while to the horses whinnying in their shack nearby.

"I wonder whether horses go to sleep," Hannah mused, "and do they sleep standing up?" She had seen horses lie down to roll. Sometimes they would roll clear over. Father said a horse was worth a hundred dollars if he could do that. Then Hannah, snuggling close to Rosetta in the manger, fell asleep.

The next day Father began making maple syrup of the sap he had gathered and boiled before they came.

"It ought to make extra-fine syrup," Father said. "The sap is sweeter when there is plenty of sunshine the summer before the trees are tapped."

He used the first sap he had gathered to make syrup because it would be nice and light colored. The darker maple sugar would be made from the rest of the sap.

The next morning the making of the maple sugar began.

72

Father boiled and skimmed and boiled and skimmed. Sometimes he had to rake the fire away from under the two big kettles if he thought the maple sugar was going to burn. When it was nearly done he tested it in a little cold water.

"Let us have a taste," Hannah pleaded.

"Wait until it cools," warned Father.

The sample cooled into the right consistency for maple sugar and was given to the children. Then Father dipped out the syrup into pans which were just large enough to make a two-pound cake. He also filled many small patty-pans. These little cakes he would sell in town for five cents each. Now the children scraped the kettle. And was it good!

One day, toward evening, while Father was watching the bubbling kettles of syrup, some Indians who had been hunting in the woods below Elk Run came begging for maple sugar. Above the trees of the sugar bush they had seen the thin spiral of smoke that drifted away to the southeast. They had smelled the fragrant, sweetish odor that arose from the steaming sap as it boiled violently in the kettles. Father gave each one several of the little scalloped cakes. They grunted their approval and went on down the river.

At the end of the week, when all the maple syrup and sugar had been made, it was time to break camp. All the tiny cakes of sugar lay packed in Father's leather trunk. How nice the till of the trunk looked before he shut the lid—rows and rows of little scalloped pans, all evenly packed.

"It has been a good week," said Father.

They loaded everything into the wagon—even the boat they had come in! Father and Mother, Julia and Harlan sat on the spring seat. Hannah, Rosetta, and Cornelia were on the trunk filled with the little pans of maple sugar. How people stared as they drove across the bridge and through town! The girls felt very important. They had been helping to make maple sugar. But perhaps, thought Hannah, perhaps the wagon with the long boat sticking out of the back was what people were really looking at!

10

An Indian Scare

A few thousand Sac and Fox Indians still lived in Iowa in 1845 which was the year the George Hannas, the first permanent settlers, arrived at Prairie Rapids. As a result of a treaty with the Government, some twenty-four hundred Sacs and Foxes had promised to move to Kansas that year. They had sold their land to the Government for about twelve cents an acre. But they loved their Iowa hunting grounds, so they didn't leave immediately, just stayed and hunted as they had done for years before.

Later, when they did move into Kansas, they were dissatisfied. It was hot and dry there, and they said the water made them sick. They were homesick and longed for the cool shade along the Iowa streams. They remembered the good hunting—the deer, wild turkey, otter, muskrat, and raccoons. Groups of them came back to hunt and fish and trap.

Every spring, when the ice broke up and the warm April days came, the Kansas Indians grew restless. Tribe by tribe they kept wandering back to their former haunts in Iowa, following the Indian trails, many of which were old buffalo paths. They trekked to the Cedar River for fish and game and to set their traps in the woods nearby.

It was a curious sight to see them coming, single file, as they always traveled. At the head of the column rode the old chief. The strings of beads he wore around his neck reached from his ears to his shoulder. One of the chiefs was such a big fellow that when he rode his Indian pony his feet almost touched the ground. It was the wise old chief who told the company when to stop and where to camp.

The Indian braves followed, riding their ponies. The squaws, many of them with papooses on their backs, trudged along behind on foot. They wore dresses of deer hide under their blankets, and their hair hung down their backs in two braids. They did all the work around the camp, and the bucks or braves, as the men were called, provided the food by hunting and fishing. If any corn were raised or gardening done, the squaws did the planting and hoeing. They also dressed the meat when it was brought in from the hunt.

An Indian Scare

The Indians used a travois to haul their tepees, or other Indian belongings, from place to place. A travois was a kind of trailer and was made of two poles fastened to a platform that dragged on the ground. The tepees and bundles were transported on this platform. One end of each pole was tied to an Indian pony's breast collar and girth which were made of braided elm bark or deer hide.

When they made camp, the squaws set up the tepees. Over some poles tied together at the top and spreading out in a circle they stretched buffalo skins that hung to the ground. The Indian men would immediately start out to set their traps, to fish, or to hunt for wild turkey, prairie chickens, or quail. Often the squaws would go to the cabins of the settlers to beg for flour and lard and milk. They also wanted salt to salt down the fish and muskrat the braves would bring back to camp.

One day two Indian squaws came to Mother Baker's door to beg. As always, they walked right in without knocking. One was a young squaw with her papoose strapped to a board that hung on her back. At the top was a kind of hood to protect the baby's head and shade its eyes. At the bottom was a piece of wood for its feet to rest on. This was the baby's cradle. It was lined with bark and made soft with deerskin. When the squaws came in, the younger one set the board with the papoose down in a corner of the room.

Mother Baker went to the summer kitchen to get a slab of side meat, for every pioneer family had its own pork barrel. When she came back, she laid the meat on the long puncheon table and cut it into two pieces, for she had learned from the other settlers that she must give each Indian something, no matter how many there were, instead of giving it all to one of them.

As she handed one piece of meat to the old squaw, who grunted her approval, the young one jumped up and grabbed the other piece. This vexed Mother Baker and, although she was a frail little woman weighing only ninety pounds, she shook the young squaw and set her down in a chair.

"Brave squaw! Brave squaw!" the old squaw said, getting up and patting Mother on the shoulder. Just then, happening to look out the window, Mother saw a half-dozen big Indian braves walking single file around the barn. She was frightened, indeed, and didn't feel at all like a "brave squaw." Trying not to show her fear, she hunted up a blanket and a cornhusk doll for the little papoose and gave each squaw some flour, which pleased them immensely. They then left without calling to their braves.

When an Indian was a friend, he was a true friend. But if a white man cheated or wronged him in any way, the Indian became angry not only at this one person, but at the whole white race. Because of this characteristic, there were many Indian "scares." Many a night Father and Mother Baker took turns sitting at the window watching for Indians while the rest of the family slept.

One day a man came riding his horse on the run to warn the people of the settlement to be on their guard.

"The Indians are on the warpath!" he shouted. "I have seen their campfires near here."

One man was so frightened he loaded his family into their prairie schooner and drove away.

As it happened Father Baker had gone to Dubuque that day to sell a load of wheat and bring back supplies for the winter. He was not expected home that night. Hannah rose bravely to the occasion.

"We'll all sleep in the loft tonight," she said. "And we'll take the ax with us. No Indian will get up there alive, for I'll split his head open!"

In the night they heard someone moving about downstairs. Hannah was wide-awake and ready. Soon she heard him begin to crawl up the ladder to the loft. Standing over the hatchway with the ax in her hand, Hannah waited. As his head came up to the opening, and Hannah's mother saw by the moonlight the ax ready to strike, she screamed.

"What's the matter?" the voice from the ladder called out. It was Father Baker. Mother's scream had saved his life.

11

Scrubbing the Floor

By 1858 the Bakers had torn down the log cabin and built a frame house. There were plenty of mills now to supply the demands for lumber.

Mother Baker took great pride in her new home. The parlor had a rag carpet tacked tight up against the wall. And was it hard to stretch and tack down! Especially in the fall, for then they put straw under it to keep the floor warmer. Wood-burning stoves didn't heat the floors very much.

After the carpet had been tacked down on one end and one side the stretching began. Starting at the one side that had been already tacked, Father Baker came slowly across the room, scuffing his feet to bring up a little more slack while Mother, down on her hands and knees, drove in the tacks.

The parlor bedroom had a rag carpet, too. The bedroom off the kitchen had some homemade braided rugs. The kitchen floor, though, was always bare, and how Mother Baker did have to scrub to keep it clean! One day she had some unexpected help.

Rosetta and Cornelia had a little friend, Annie Jennings, who lived right next door. My! the good times they had playing together in a playhouse they had made with some boards placed across the top of the fence in the corner of the Bakers' back yard. And oh, the fine mud pies they made out there!

One day when the two mothers and Hannah had gone to a quilting party, Annie was staying with the Baker girls. Annie was all excited because her mother had decided to let her go to the private school a Miss Mattie Hoskinson was going to hold that summer in an abandoned log cabin not far from the Baker home. It cost a dollar a term, Annie said. She talked and talked about it—and of course she wanted Cornelia and Rosetta to ask their mother to let them go, too.

"I'll tell you what let's do," Annie said at last. "Let's do something that will please your mother so much she'll say you can go."

For a long time they couldn't decide on anything that would please her enough.

"I know what let's do," Rosetta said at last. "Let's scrub the floor. That'll please her!"

Cornelia got the broom while Rosetta went down cellar for some soft soap. She told Annie her mother always put soft soap on the grease spots around the stove.

"Well, look here." Annie pointed to some spots near the table. "We ought to put some soap on them." So Rosetta went downstairs for another pan of soap.

"Let's make it awful white," Cornelia said. "Let's make it whiter than it's ever been before!"

"Then let's put soap all over the floor," said Annie. And after many trips to the old keg in the cellar they had the floor well plastered with soft soap.

They were all barefooted. Soon their toes began to smart so from the lye in the soap that they started for the water pail to pour the water over their smarting feet. But they had so much soap on the floor that it was the slipperiest place you ever saw! Their feet slid out from under them every which way. They fell down, tried to get up, and fell again. At last they got to the pail and dipped the water over their feet with the big, long-handled dipper. Then they ran out to the well to windlass up another bucket of water.

It was one of those old-fashioned, "old-oaken-bucket" wells. They turned the handle of a windlass to let the rope lower the bucket into the water and then turned the handle the other way so that the rope would haul up the bucket of water.

Well, they carried water and they scrubbed and they scrubbed and they scrubbed. But the more water they put on the floor the more the soap lathered and the harder it was to keep from falling down.

What a time they had! They slipped and they slid; they scrubbed and they scrubbed. But the more water they put on the floor the worse it got.

The day was hot. They were so warm and tired and exasperated they wanted to give up. But they knew they had to get that soap off some way before their mothers and Hannah got home. Forgetting their smarting feet, they carried more and more pails of water and scrubbed frantically, always sweeping the foaming suds out the back door till the back stoop, the walk, and even part of the yard were fairly swimming with it!

They were just in the midst of it all when their mothers and Hannah came home. Of course they wanted to know what the children meant by wasting so much soft soap. They were so excited they took the brooms and scrubbed and scrubbed, too. And every minute of the time they scolded. To think they had wasted all that soap!

After Annie and her mother had gone home, Mother Baker went to the cellar to see how much they had used. When she came up she said they had used nearly half a keg of soap! And, oh dear, the lye in the soap was turning the floor—not white—but as yellow as an old duck's foot! When Rosetta and Cornelia had the courage to glance up at their mother's face, they knew that this was no time to mention enrolling in Miss Mattie Hoskinson's private school.

12

School Days

BEFORE the day came for the private school to open, Mother had heard about it and decided to let the girls go. Julia was eight years old now and here was an opportunity to send her to a school near their home.

The first thing the settlers had done after building their log cabins was to build a cabin for a church on Sunday and school during the week. That was in 1853. That was where Rosetta and Cornelia went to school. Hannah, too, had gone there the first few years, but it was a long way from the Baker cabin and here was an opportunity for all three girls to go nearby.

On the opening day in the little old log hut, there was the teacher, Miss Mattie Hoskinson, standing at the front of the room, reading some verses from the Bible. The children could feel the rough-hewn bench of split logs under them while they sang, "Dare to be a Daniel." Then they sat humped over their books with no desks to rest them on, no backs to the seats. When they finished studying a book, they laid it down beside them on the bench.

The log cabin stood on Bluff Street, right beside Dan Flannigan's lime kiln, a stone building in which crushed rock was burned to make lime. Strayer's brickyard had been started, and masons needed lime in making mortar. The whitewash that pioneers used instead of paint was made of lime, too. Often Mother Baker sent one of the girls to the lime kiln to buy five cents' worth of lime so she could whitewash the kitchen ceiling. When it was dried, it was as white as chalk and gave the room a sweet, fresh smell.

It was at the little private school that Cornelia swallowed a pin—or thought she did. The deep window sills were a nice place to sit and eat lunch. One day the girls were sitting there with their lunch baskets beside them. Whatever made Cornelia do it she never could tell afterward, but she put a bent pin on one side of the piece of bread she was eating and thought she would see how many bites it would take to get around to the pin. Something took her attention and before she knew it she was past the place where the pin was. She was sure she had swallowed it! She coughed and cried and made such a noise that all the pupils gathered around her and the teacher was about ready to send someone to bring her mother. However, during the excitement one of the older boys had sense enough to get down on the floor and look for the pin— and found it!

At this time the West Side Grade School was in process of building. In the fall of 1860 it was finished and all the Baker children were happy. Julia was put in the fifth grade. How she loved her teacher, Mary Pratt. On the first floor a box stove, in the front of the room, burned cordwood. When the little children came to school half-frozen, Miss Pratt would rub their hands and not let them get too near the fire until they gradually got warm. While this went on the children could hear the boys who were in the upper grades go clumping up the stairs with frozen boots. They called them "frozen" because the leather in their boots became stiff as a board from walking so far through the deep snow.

How mischievous some of the boys were! Sometimes they'd gather some sneezewort, called sneezeweed, from the prairie and hide it in their pockets. And just before they came into the schoolhouse they'd put a little in their noses. In a minute they'd all begin to sneeze!

One night the Bakers were awakened by noise and excitement outdoors. The schoolhouse was on fire! Hannah leaped to her feet and tried to light the lamp. It wouldn't light because Mother Baker had forgotten to fill it with kerosene. When Hannah took it out on the back porch there was so much light from the burning building that she could fill the lamp as easily as in the daytime.

There was a big crowd in the street and the firemen were working on the engine. It was four blocks to the river, and the fire engine couldn't force the water that far. Men and women formed a line and tried to pass pails of water from the river to the schoolhouse, but the fire was soon out of control. The red flames licked the windows; glass clattered to the ground. The roar of the fire grew louder, and so did the tumult in the street and hoarse shouting of men. The flames went from one story to the next, and at last they reached the little dome on top of the building. The schoolhouse was gone! Julia had brought one book home, her precious McGuffey's Fifth Reader. All the rest burned.

During the next year, while the schoolhouse was being rebuilt, school was held in several buildings about the town. Some of the grades were housed in the Congregational church. At that time only the basement had been completed and the floor above was used as a granary. Because of the grain, the mice were "thicker than spatter." The children enjoyed watching these shy little creatures more than the teachers did. Anna Perry, one of the primary teachers, said she was going to have her skirts trimmed around the bottom with mousetraps instead of embroidery! And Julia told Hannah that, of course, she wasn't afraid of mice, but just the same she was glad to be wearing high-button shoes!

After the new schoolhouse was built, Professor von Coellen was the superintendent. He was a big, heavy man with rough hair that tumbled about his head. He often came into one of the upper grades when the arithmetic class had its problems worked out on the blackboard. He would listen while a pupil with a long-handled pointer in one hand pointed out each step in the solution of a problem. Woe betide the pupil if he missed a step! The professor's chief delight was a drill in mental arithmetic. He made this seem as much fun as a game.

The eighth-grade teacher, Miss Harbin, with her red hair and rosy cheeks, was fine-looking, but there was one thing about her that the pupils never liked.

"Answer 'perfect' or 'imperfect,'" she would say as she called the roll at night. "Did you whisper today? Answer truthfully!"

"My!" thought Rosetta. "It really isn't fair to have to tattle on yourself."

13

Christmas Visitors

ONE cold day—it was the day before Christmas—Rosetta and Cornelia were busy churning some butter in the old stone churn. Cornelia pushed the dasher up and down through the hole in the churn lid fifty times. Then Rosetta took her turn. The little bubbles rose up around the dasher and piled over each other. Over and over they churned and counted and watched the bubbles. Finally little white coagulated specks began to appear around the dasher.

"Mama," Cornelia called, "the butter's coming."

"All right," answered her mother. "Keep on going for a minute or two, then I'll gather it for you."

She had just gone to get some cold water to put in the churn to help gather the butter particles when a bobsled full of people drove up in front of the house. It was an old friend of Father Baker with his family. They were the Kelleys, on their way to a farm they had bought near Buckingham, Iowa.

Father and Mother Baker welcomed them heartily, and Father helped unload the five children two of whom were practically babies. He brought them in and put them on the flat-bottomed bed lounge, and the Baker girls began to take their hoods off.

"I thought I better not go any farther tonight," Mr. Kelley said. "There's a storm brewing and the house will be cold when we get there."

"It's brewing all right, Henry," Father Baker agreed. "It's beginning to snow already, and the wind's coming up fast. Come right in, all of you. We're always glad to see an old friend, and make new ones, too."

After all the wraps were off, Mother Baker hugged the babies and said some pleasant words to the three older children. Then she asked Mrs. Kelley if she would like to come into the kitchen and talk while she finished working over her butter.

Father had taken his friend into the front room. Mrs. Kelley sat in the kitchen, the baby on her lap and the little three-year-old trying to climb up, too. Soon she began pouring out her heart to Mother Baker about moving in the wintertime, this "fool idea," she called it. She said she had seen enough of this wilderness of prairie land.

But Mr. Kelley had told her, she said, to wait and see where they were going to live. It was a beautiful place, for the house stood on a bluff overlooking a small stream that held plenty of water in all seasons.

"What are you going to raise on the farm?" asked Mother.

"Oh, it's a sheep farm," replied Mrs. Kelley. "And there's fruit there, too—especially grapes. Henry says it's the prettiest place you ever saw. You can look down from the house and see the grapevines climbing all over the trees along the little stream."

"Sounds like rather wild country to me," remarked Mother. "But I've heard it was hilly around Buckingham."

It was nearing suppertime. There was a little hotel on Commercial Street—the Sherman House—that served good meals for twenty-five cents, but the Bakers wouldn't think of sending anyone to a hotel to eat, whether seven people or twice that many dropped in unexpectedly to spend the night and Christmas.

There was enough food but Mother Baker was wondering just how she was going to manage the sleeping arrangements. However, by the time she had worked the butter into a loaf with a clover-leaf design, which she cleverly made with the butter ladle, she had figured them out. She would send the men to the little hotel just to sleep.

But how was she going to provide Christmas presents for five little children? She kept seeing five little empty stockings hanging beside her own children's stockings.

After she and Father had had a consultation in the pantry, she said to Mrs. Kelley, "It's just a short piece over

93

to the hotel. Let's let the older children go along with the men for the fun of it. Father is driving over to see if he can get a reservation for himself and Mr. Kelley tonight. I can accommodate you and all the children here."

As soon as they were gone, Mother told Cornelia and Rosetta they could make some popcorn balls. They were delighted. Mother went upstairs with Mrs. Kelley to show her where to put the babies to sleep and when she came down, she had her hands full of little remnants of new cloth and some old cotton stockings whose feet were past mending—the children's old Sunday white ones and week-day black ones.

Then she sat down and it wasn't long till she had some rag dolls cut out. Hannah came to help, and they took shape in record time. Meanwhile Mrs. Kelley was stuffing some cloth cats made of old white stockings. She proved to be an artist at drawing cat patterns. Before the men brought the children back there were three of the best-dressed little doll babies ever seen, and four clever cats with eyes, nose, and whiskers embroidered with bits of yarn. The popcorn balls had been finished, too, and everything had been whisked away before they saw the bobsled driving up.

Mother Baker asked Mrs. Kelley to entertain the children in the front room, and when the door was closed, she told the men she had a project for them. Immediately she brought out a little sack of empty spools. Father Baker was handy with a jackknife, she knew, and before long the two men were spinning some cunning little tops around on the

94

kitchen table. Mother was getting supper and Hannah was setting the table.

After what seemed to the children a long time, supper was over and they all crowded into the bobsled. It was snowing hard but the wind had died down somewhat. Anyway, a blizzard couldn't keep the people in town away from the Christmas tree in those days.

When they went into the church, there on the platform stood the most wonderful Christmas tree—ever so high and decorated with strings of popcorn and lighted with home-made candles donated by the mothers. In the summertime, when they made candles, they dipped a dozen or more small ones especially for the Sunday-school Christmas tree. The candles were set in little tin holders that snapped onto the twigs of the tree.

From every branch hung presents for the children: dolls of all sizes, little wooden carts, whistles, wooden guns, balls, and wooden blocks. Mother had given her contribution of toys to an usher at the door as they went in and they were soon on the tree.

On the floor at the side of the tree stood a big bucket of sand and a pail of water, just in case the flame from a candle set the tree afire.

The Baker and Kelley children went down the aisle to the front seats to join the chattering little folks who were waiting for the program to begin. Every child was trying to pick out his or her present on the tree. During all the talking and wriggling and standing up and sitting down some girls spied a little table sitting under the tree. Then there was more buzzing than ever.

"Oh, I do want that little table!" said the little girl sitting next to Julia.

"It ought to be for me," insisted a girl who was leaning over her shoulder, "because I have a set of little dishes. You could bring your doll and come over to my house and we'd play tea party."

Soon the time came for the program of Christmas songs, recitations, and dialogues. Each girl in Julia's class spoke a stanza about the dear Saviour born in a manger in Bethlehem. Harlan's recitation told of the angel's message to the shepherds as they watched their flock of sheep that night on the Judean hillside, and the sudden appearance of a multitude of the heavenly host with the angel, praising God and saying, "Glory to God in the highest and on earth peace, good will toward men."

As the glorious Christmas message was told that night in song and story the Christmas tree, every branch bending with the weight of its burden of toys, was almost forgotten. But when the program was finished there was a general stir of expectancy.

The superintendent of the Sunday school came to the platform. He picked up a basket of popcorn balls and sacks of Christmas candy and nuts, and called for his helpers to come and pass them out.

Then he turned to the tree. He asked for two ladders and two men to climb them to get the presents off the tree.

96

They handed them down to other men. As the superintendent received the presents and read off the names, he had something to say to each child. Children were skipping up the aisle and coming back holding their treasured toy and smiling broadly. The girl sitting next to Julia did get the little table she wanted. Such a happy time!

At last it was over, and the Bakers with their friends were home again. And still there was something wonderful to look forward to. All the children in the house that night came trooping downstairs to fasten their stockings to the stout string stretched along the edge of the wide clock shelf. Those empty stockings hanging in a row wouldn't be hanging there so limply in the morning. Every child knew that!

Sure enough, in the morning they were crammed with apples and nuts and popcorn balls and homemade candy, each piece wrapped in paper and tied with a red string. And there were dolls, tops, and stuffed cats besides.

Santa Claus had come just as the children expected and found enough presents in his pack for all the little Kelleys as well as the Bakers. And he left them a note with a little joke about finding so many extra children at this house this year! What a jolly Santa Claus! He loved them all!

Mother Baker had prepared an especially nice Christmas dinner: a roasted wild turkey, a big tureen of mashed potatoes, crabapple pickles, watermelon preserves, and last of all mince pie. There was enough for everybody. The children felt like little stuffed dolls themselves. But this

97

time there were no leftovers for the next day as there usually were at the Baker house after a Christmas or Thanksgiving dinner.

It had stopped snowing. Blizzards that came in December weren't so bad. The worst ones would come in January or February about the time of the full moon, Father said.

Right after dinner Mr. Kelley said he thought they'd better start out. He knew, of course, that if he couldn't get through the drifts, they would be welcome at any home along the way. And so they all said "Good-by and Happy New Year." What a nice pioneer Christmas it had been!

14

The Circus Comes to Town

AFTER the Bakers had been in Waterloo about eight years a very wonderful thing happened. The railroad came through the little settlement. It was on March 11, 1861, that the first passenger train on the Dubuque and Sioux City Railroad arrived in Waterloo from Dubuque. There was plenty of excitement that day. All the people who had given money to get the railroad to come had been promised a free ride.

The mothers had warned the children to stand far back from the tracks when the train came in. "If you don't," they warned, "the suction from the engine will draw you

99

right under the train." Long before the train came small boys laid crossed pins on the rails so that when the wheels of the train ran over them they would be flattened together like a pair of little scissors.

The engine was very small compared with railroad engines today, and so were the coaches, but the children were all standing way back at a safe distance when the train came in blowing steam and smoke.

After the railroad arrived the village grew to 1,800 people, large enough to attract a circus. All the boys of the little town got up at four o'clock in the morning and went down below basketmaker Williams' place and sat along the road waiting for Yankee Robinson's Circus to come in. The circus wagons had driven all night over the muddy roads and were late getting in. Some of the boys were sitting there almost asleep when someone yelled out, "Here they come!" All jumped up and ran alongside the gilded wagons to see what they could. The cages were open a little to give the animals air. There were leopards and lions and tigers and llamas, which look a little like camels, and come from South America.

To see the circus unload was a wonderful treat. The boys followed along till they got to the show grounds down below Father Baker's home. When the keepers took the elephants down to the river to drink, what fun the boys had watching them roll and squeal and shoot water with their long trunks!

What an exciting place it was! So many men running about, each getting his part of the work done as quickly as

100

possible. Some took care of the dogs and the ponies and the horses. Others put up the big circus tent and the cook tent. Two men to a post alternately swung their big heavy sledge hammers, and the rhythmical strokes drove in the big posts to which the tents would be tied. Next, the canvas sides went up, and then the big canopy top with its scalloped valance.

All the Bakers went to the circus performance. As they arrived, the ticket seller in his high stand was calling out to the crowd to buy tickets. The barkers were crying out the wonders of the side shows: the sword swallower, the bearded lady, the snake charmer, the midgets, and the fat lady. It was a hot day, and a boy ran about as the crowd came in selling palm-leaf fans to the women.

"Here's a fan," he'd call out. "If you don't want it, lady, feed it to the elephant."

When the Bakers finally got into the big tent, it was so crowded they couldn't find a place where they could all sit together. But at last Father located some seats high up, two on the top row and one just below. He told Mother to take the smaller children and sit up there where they could see better. He and Hannah and Rosetta found some seats farther down. Mother had Julia on one side of her and Harlan on the other. Cornelia sat in front of Julia.

Soon everyone was watching the entrance for the first glimpse of the grand procession. First of all in came the performing dogs. Suddenly everyone "o-o-ohed" and "a-a-ahed," for after the dogs some cute monkeys appeared, riding on the backs of handsome ponies. Then came the fancy bareback riders on their white horses; and next the funny clowns in their big baggy suits and pointed caps, their faces white as chalk and their noses flaming red.

The caged animals were next, and all at once the lion roared, scaring all the children. Last of all a camel and an elephant plodded in. While these were parading around the ring, some tightrope walkers ran into the center of the tent, bowed, and then climbed ladders to a platform, ready to start their act.

All went well with Mother and the children up on the top seats of the tent until the elephants began to perform. When they arranged themselves in the shape of a pyramid upon a platform, Cornelia got so excited she jumped right up. This overbalanced Julia whose feet happened to be on the back of Cornelia's dress. Up they flew. Because she was on the top row of seats, there was nothing to hold her, and over she went backward down onto the ground quicker than anyone can say Jack Robinson!

Mother screamed, and there was a great commotion. Father crawled under the seats and picked Julia up. The breath was knocked out of her, and he carried her unconscious out of the tent.

She wasn't hurt much, however. In a few minutes she came to, but her hat was gone. Father looked all over after everyone had gone out of the tent but couldn't find it anywhere. Could an elephant have eaten it up?

But Mother didn't care about the hat. She was glad the child hadn't been killed. She said she had had enough of circuses to last her a long time!

15

The Westsiders
Go to the Tournament

THAT spring a freshet washed away the greater part of
Fourth Street bridge. While the bridge was being re-
placed, the ferry was put into service again. It crossed the
river farther up, at Second Street. The fare was five cents.

Now it happened that this very summer a fireman's
tournament was to be held on the fairgrounds on the east
side of the river. The Westsiders began talking about some
other way to get across the river. When the whole family
wanted to go for three days so as not to miss any of the

races, five cents a person counted up, and money was scarce in those early days.

The Eastsiders said they didn't see why the Westsiders were making such a fuss. Eastsiders had to cross the river every day to get their mail at the post office on the west side! And, besides, when the last circus came to town, it showed on the west side! There was always a lot of bickering between the Eastsiders and the Westsiders. By hook or by crook, one side was always trying to get ahead of the other. Now if it had only been wintertime, everyone could have walked across on the ice.

At last they found a solution. They built a bridge—a footbridge in about three hours one evening! It happened this way. The Illinois Central machine shops had been moved here from Dubuque a short time before. A gang of shopmen volunteered to put the bridge across after working hours.

During the day lumber had been piled on the riverbank. After supper, when the men arrived with hammers and saws, they started the bridge from the east side where the lumber had been piled. This was below the dam, where the ford used to be, and where the river was lowest. If it hadn't been there, the bridge couldn't have been built so quickly.

Just as the men started working, along came the band! This served two purposes. It inspired the workers and it called a crowd together. After working all day the shopmen were tired, naturally. With the band playing on the shore, though, the whole town turned out to see what was going on. Even the storekeepers watched from their doors and windows. The stores were always open in the evening in those days.

With the citizens cheering, the band playing, and the hammers pound-pound-pounding out over the water, the shopmen forgot their fatigue, pitched in, and put on a show that almost equaled the tournament itself!

There had been a lot of curiosity all day about what was to be done with all the lumber piled on the east river bank. Now everyone saw the bridge taking shape, the two-by-fours in pairs being driven into the river at equal distances, and a board nailed across each pair, till the river looked as though a lot of carpenter's sawhorses were strung across it. When two planks were nailed on top, the people saw a bridge wide enough to walk across single file. The workmen fastened a railing on one side in case anyone got dizzy going across. After it was finished, some people thought it was really a dizzy-looking bridge! They didn't get it built straight across the river for one thing. And since the river bed was so uneven, it made the bridge wavy-like—up and down.

It wasn't much of a bridge, and the first high water washed it away, but it served its purpose. The Westsiders, men, women, and children, holding on to the railing, trooped across.

What a wonderful three days of fun everyone had at the tournament! Fire and hose companies with their bands in bright uniforms were there from all the largest towns around—Dubuque, Cedar Rapids, and Marshalltown. There were hose-cart-pulling races to see which company could run the fastest; there were pumping contests in which each company strove to throw the highest stream of water with their fire engines, and there was a coupling race in which men from different companies competed to see who could couple the hose to the fire engine the quickest.

Even the young boys about twelve years of age were in the tournament, for they had a small hand engine that Clarence Hollister had just made for them. They named it the Water Lily, and were proud that it could throw water a hundred feet. These boys had a drum corps, too, and how fine all the boys looked in their new white uniforms trimmed with red!

In those early days it was considered a great honor to belong to a fire company or its band. Those boys were always popular with the girls, probably because of their nice-looking uniforms. The competition between the west and east side in their uniforms and in their equipment was very keen. For instance, all the Westsiders were proud of their good-looking firemen in red jackets, caps, and white gloves. And they were proud that their hand fire engine had been bought in Chicago for a *thousand dollars!*

When the preliminaries were over and the final contests completed, none of the other towns had won a single first place. The Westsiders were first in the hose-cart-pulling race. The Eastsiders, however, had recently purchased

106

a new fire engine called the Water Witch. With this they won the pumping contest. But for all that, the Westsiders scored the big victory, for who won the coupling contest? A Westsider! Dutch Myers from the Red Jacket Hose Company!

16

The Civil War

PRESIDENT LINCOLN's message of 1861 startled the Iowa town: "Our flag has been fired on! Seventy-five thousand troops are wanted at once."

Excitement ran high. War meetings were held. One evening there was an unusually large crowd because a colored man was to speak, Fred Douglas, a Negro orator who went about helping President Lincoln get recruits. After the speeches and stirring war songs, men would go up and enlist in the army.

The children of the village watched the soldiers marching and training in the street. They learned all the com-

mands. Then they got up a children's company. The most
coveted privilege was to be the flag-bearer and march ahead.
Next came a boy beating a drum. The captain followed,
giving orders to the little company which was trying so
hard to keep in step.

"Shoulder arms; right-about-face; forward march!" These
orders were taken very seriously. On "Double quick, single file," they'd run like little Indians.

One day Mr. Parker received word that his two boys,
who were in training at Dubuque, were to go by steamboat
down the Mississippi to an unknown point in the South.
Their mother fixed up a nice box of good things to eat and
their sisters went to Dubuque to see them off. Although
they found the boys, they had time to talk to them only
a few minutes.

"We have to go now," the young men said. "We are to
parade around town before going to the boat. You girls
keep the box till we see you at the pier."

Men in uniform seem to look much alike. When they
are marching four abreast, it's very easy to miss seeing the
one you are looking for. When the girls saw that the soldiers were marching up the gangplank onto the boat without breaking ranks, they were afraid that their brothers
would pass by before they could recognize them and hand
them the box. They told the commanding officer their di-
lemma, and he promised to call the boys' name and have
them fall out of rank.

"Parker! Parker!" called the officer frequently. But the
whole line marched by and not a man turned his head!

The girls didn't know whether the boys didn't hear their name called or whether they felt so bad at leaving they didn't want to speak to their sisters again. The girls never found out why they missed their brothers.

But one day there came a message—one of the boys had been killed in the battle of Pea Ridge. Later, the other boy died of fever in a hospital. These were sad, trying days in their home. Mr. Parker sold his farm and invested all the money in government bonds. If the South had won the war, the bonds would have been worthless, but he wanted to do his part to help the North.

During the long war everyone suffered—those who stayed at home almost as much as the men who went to the front, because they were always fearful of sad news of their loved ones—of relatives missing, sick, wounded, or, worst of all, killed in action. John Ward, a young man the Bakers knew well, was reported killed. After the message came his father walked the floor all night. But there had been a mistake—John came back at the close of the war. It was another John Ward who had been killed.

Of course there were some living here in the North who were not loyal. There were a few families who sympathized with the South. In Waterloo there was one man whom Father Baker considered the worst of all—at least he did the most talking. He was called an old "Secessionist." That meant he thought the South should separate from the North. One day some soldiers who were home on furlough went to his house by the river to see him.

"We want you to hurrah for the Union," they said, "or we're going to duck you in the river!"

They ducked him. "Will you hurrah for the Union now?" the soldiers would ask every time they brought him up out of the water.

But he was such a stubborn old fellow, they had to duck him so many times that he was about drowned before he gave in. At last he was glad to shout for the Union. Maybe he wasn't any more loyal to the northern side, but after that he kept his ideas to himself.

The war really came to Iowa when Morgan came over the state line from Missouri and there was a battle on the Des Moines River. As far as Waterloo was concerned, the war came closest when the first wounded soldier was sent home and died. That was Captain Washburn. His death made the whole town like one big family, for everyone attended the funeral. It was a military one, and a large delegation came clear from Dubuque to attend it.

Many men in Iowa who were too old for active service in the army were eager to help in some way. They thought perhaps they could be used for guard duty or as stretcher-bearers and relieve younger men for service at the front. So many of these older men sent requests to Governor Kirkwood of Iowa that the Secretary of War gave the governor permission to form a regiment of men forty-five to sixty-four years of age, the Thirty-seventh Iowa Volunteer Regiment.

It was in this regiment that Father Baker enlisted. On

113

the day he left he said to Hannah, "I am proud that you are such a big, strong girl. Mother will have a good helper while I'm gone."

The captain of Father Baker's company had a funny name, Captain Hogledogle. However, he was a fine soldier and took good care of his men.

Father Baker wrote that after they had trained at Muscatine and were sent on to St. Louis, their snappy step was much admired. As they marched down the street, General Curtis said their regiment was one of the finest he had seen. But many of the men were past sixty and broke down under the hardships of war. When the army was on the march they slept on the ground wrapped in their army blankets. Often water was scarce, and the water they drank from little streams made them sick. Father Baker said he had seen men get down and drink from holes made by mules' feet sinking into the watery mud, because their throats were so parched with thirst. Iowa was the only state that had such a regiment of older men who were jokingly called "Graybeards."

Most of their work was picket duty and guarding prisoners and military prisons. They also guarded trains in railroad yards and sometimes they escorted trains. In July of 1864, while fifty of their men were guarding a supply train, they were attacked near Memphis, Tennessee, by raiders, called guerrillas. Two of the "Graybeards" were killed and two wounded, but the rest got the train through.

During the war women endured many hardships, too, but they were brave and tried to cheer and help the men at the front by sending boxes of clothing and food when they knew where their relatives were stationed. If they could, they sent money, too, for a soldier's pay was only thirteen dollars a month and he had to buy his own clothes.

When the Government could not furnish enough uniforms, the women formed societies and, under the direction of local tailors, cut and sewed the blue cloth. Once, at Dubuque, two hundred and fifty women worked for nine days making uniforms.

Mother Baker was one of the women who went about from door to door asking for pieces of old linen. They tore the cloth in strips and scraped the lint for surgeons to use to pack wounds to stop bleeding. That was before the time of sterilized dressings.

Before the war women had done scarcely any work outside the home. Now they tried to take the men's places as far as possible so that their positions would be waiting for them when they returned. Previously the salespeople in the stores had all been men. Now women took over.

Many post offices were run by women, too. It was a hard job, for when the mail came in just about the whole town came down to the post office to see whether there were any letters from the front.

One day a girl received a letter from a young soldier. Up in the corner of the envelope, where the stamp should have been, was written:

"Soldier's letter;
Put 'er through

N'er a cent
But six months due."

Hannah and her mother shared these hard times. Hannah was doing housework and taking care of some children for a woman who worked in a store. She received only a dollar a week, and prices were high. When she took five dollars downtown to buy goods for a calico dress, she came back with her pocketbook empty. Food was high, too, but prairie chickens were plentiful and the woods were full of wild crabapples.

The Bakers never forgot the day when the news came that General Lee had surrendered. Such an outburst of joy as that produced! In the evening people paraded the streets with torchlights. The band played, and everyone sang, "Glory, glory, hallelujah!"

It was so wonderful for all to have the war over. In the Baker home, Mother Baker and the children could now look forward to the day when Father would be home again.

But the end of the war had a special meaning for Hannah, for during the war she had been keeping company with a young man from Ohio, Richard Henry Lee Kennedy. Richard was dark and slim and so tall that in some of the smaller homes of the settlement he could reach up and touch the ceiling.

Hannah had met Richard at singing school and they had attended many church socials together. Richard was a carpenter like his father. Richard's father had come to Waterloo some time after the Baker family, when the town was still called Prairie Rapids. He wanted to help build cabins for the settlers and there was plenty for him and his son to do.

As soon as Father Baker came home from the war, Richard asked him for Hannah's hand in marriage. Of course Father Baker consented, for Richard was a fine young man and a great-grandson of a noted general of the Revolutionary War, General John Stark.

On that December day in 1865 many guests gathered at the Baker home for Hannah's wedding. Pastor Collins stood before the bridal couple and read the solemn marriage service. Hannah's parents' eyes filled with tears as the realization sank into their hearts that the time had come for the first break in their happy family. As they came up to congratulate the bridal pair at the close of the service, Hannah kissed her family and said, "Mother, don't cry. I'm not going far. You can see me every day."

Hannah's mother hurried to the kitchen to recover her composure and start the coffee for the refreshments. Beside the stove stood two baskets, one filled with coal and the other with potatoes which were from the root cellar and covered with black dirt. In her haste and confusion, Mother Baker filled the stove with potatoes instead of coal. Of course the refreshments were delayed. So with Mother Baker's laughing embarrassment and the general merriment of the guests it was a very happy wedding day for Hannah.

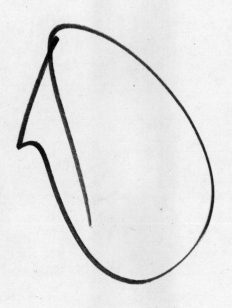